KiD YOUTUBER
HUNGRY for MORE

By Marcus Emerson

ALSO BY MARCUS EMERSON

Diary of a 6th Grade Ninja
Secret Agent 6th Grader
The Super Life of Ben Braver

This one's for Cade...

Emerson Publishing House

Book design by Marcus Emerson
Art created digitally in Clip Studio Pro.

EPISODE ONE:
STILL KIND OF A BIG DEAL

MY NAME'S DAVY SPENCER, AND YOU'RE WATCHING THE **GREATEST** YOUTUBE CHANNEL THAT NOBODY KNOWS ABOUT YET!

19 VIEWS   9 FANS

I'm back with another season of Kid YouTuber, so buckle up because this one's gonna be even BIGGER and BADDER than the last!

...but not the BAD kind of badder. The GOOD kind of badder. No, the BAD kind of badder is no good, but the GOOD kind of badder is ALL good.

Okay, "badder" sounds weird to me now. You know I'm saying BADDER, not BATTER, right? Not like cake batter or a baseball batter but... badder, like, MORE bad.

Maybe I just should've said "more bad." Words are weird.

Anyways, SO much has happened since last time that I don't even know where to start.

Oh, wait! Yes, I do! Let's start with...

Now I know what you're thinking – this probably isn't MY pool, right? Well, I promise this isn't like that one time when I said I had a thing, but the thing I was talking about wasn't actually MINE.

Nope! This pool is 100% mine... and so is the giant MANSION that's in front of it! Boo-yah!

My new place is a four-story monstrosity with 29 bedrooms, 39 bathrooms, and a ridiculous 100-car garage that's already FULL of GREEN Lamborghinis!

This house has got it all! There's a 164-seat theater where I can watch movies with all my buddies, a million-dollar hot tub that I won't ever use because hot water makes my skin itch, and TWO bowling alleys for one-on-one games without having to wait your turn!

It's got a spaceship because why not? A time machine because of course! A full T-rex skeleton because duh! And a dance club in the basement called Leap Year that's only open once every four years on February 29 because that's how the Spencer family rolls!

So, that's where I've been at for the past week, livin' the dream at my new place and floating around in my Olympic-sized swimming pool!

4

EPISODE TWO:
LET'S PLAY CATCH UP

It's been two weeks since my last video, and I'm still in my pre-famous state with my vlog, but that's okay because I'm gonna hit the big-time soon.

Since my last video, my family moved out of the El Rancho Motel and into a house. No, it's not a mansion, but it's still HOME, which is a really great thing.

The house is pretty rad, actually. There's plenty of room for my parents, my little sister (Krissy), and her blind dog (Bo-bo).

I don't have to share a bed with my sis anymore, thank goodness. Not that she's bad or anything, but I like having my own space, y'know?

Plus, after she became a YouTube star, she's been way super annoying. Ever since the video of her tea party with Bo-bo went viral, she's been a different person. She let fame go to her head. When my videos go viral someday, I promise I won't go all ROCKSTAR like that.

Just look at her...

THIS CHOCOLATE SANDWICH IS CUT IN HALF AND STILL HAS THE CRUST! I SAID LEAVE IT BIG AND CUT THE CRUST!

Our house is about a block away from the old motel, which if you remember, is actually where my best friend, Chuck Metropolis, lives because his parents own it. Well, they don't live AT the motel but in a house ATTACHED to the motel.

Chuck spends his days playing Minecraft and practicing sweet ninjas moves in the woods behind the motel. I asked him why he's training so hard to be a ninja (besides being just an awesome hobby), and he said it was better to be prepared than unprepared, whatever that means.

I mean, don't get me wrong – if there's ever a zombie apocalypse, I'll be the first one standing behind Chuck as he kicks some zombie booty.

My other best friend, Annie Yun, lives right next to the motel. She's all artsy and stuff, drawing all day long in sketchbooks. She's super good at it, probably the best in town.

So, yeah, we're all in the same neighborhood, which RULES because it's really easy for us to hang out still.

Let me give you a quick tour of the new digs. It's one-story, three-bedrooms. Cozy, but not small. The yard is big enough to throw a football around, but small enough that it doesn't take forever to mow.

Plenty of trees. A roof. Some windows. There's a bathroom. With a toilet. There's a kitchen...

A sink...

Some counter tops...

A garbage disposal, I don't know.

What else is there to say?

House tours are boring unless you're an adult. The first thing my parents do with our guests is give them a tour of the place, like they care about what our bathroom looks like.

That's just weird if you ask me.

7

There's also an attic that MIGHT or MIGHT NOT be haunted. It's one of those attics you can climb up to through a hatch in the ceiling. Just pull a little string, and a ladder unfolds.

Sometimes, in the middle of the night, I hear scratching sounds coming from up there like something's trying to get out.

Creepy, right?

I told my dad about it, but when he checked, he didn't see anything. He thinks it might've been some kind of animal – a BAT or something, like THAT'S supposed to help me feel better about closing my eyes at night.

I asked if it could be a ghost, but he shut that idea down right away. He said it's def not a ghost because there's no such thing, but isn't that exactly what ghosts WANT you to think – that they don't exist??

We've also got a creek in our backyard. Well, technically, it's just past our property line, so it's not in OUR backyard.

It's the CITY'S backyard.

My mom wants to put a fence up to block it off. She thinks it's dangerous because the creek is nestled in at the bottom of a gully.

*Sidenote – I didn't know what a GULLY was until I made this video. It's, like, a trench that's been worn into the earth by running water.

**Sidenote for the sidenote – a trench is like a long, narrow ditch. Remember at the end of Star Wars when Luke is flying his X-wing in that huge gutter thing right before he blows the Death Star up? Yeah, THAT'S a trench.

So, basically, we've got this TRENCH in our backyard that's pretty deep. Like, DEEP, deep. Deep enough that if you fell into it, you'd probably break a million different bones you didn't know you had.

Oh, and there's one more thing I forgot to mention about my new place. Something awful. Terrible. Just the WORST.

It's the only thing I hate about the house. And it's not so much the house itself, but WHERE the house is located. Like, WHOSE house is right next door.

I'll give you ten bucks if you can guess who lives next to me.

No, nevermind, I don't have that kind of money.

I'll just tell you...

Fergus.

Freakin.

Widdershim.

Yup.

Out of ALL the houses we could've moved into, we had to move into the one next to the Widdershim family.

Fergus is 10 years old, in 6th grade, and he's got the most popular YouTube channel at the school.

And when I say that out loud, it sounds like we should be BFFs, right? But we're not. Rivals can't be BFFs. He's my competition and I'm his, so don't listen to whatever he tells you about me. We're secret enemies!

Lowkey, the kid hates me and wants to see my YouTube channel crash and burn. You know it. I know it. We ALL seem to know it except for him!

And as if living next door to Fergus wasn't bad enough, our bedroom windows literally face each other. He's the last thing I see every night and the first thing I see every morning, so every time I look outside, I see this...

I don't have curtains yet, so I can't exactly block him out of my life. He constantly writes messages on sheets of paper, then holds them up in his window for me to read.

I only have one sheet of paper for my answer to him.

EPISODE THREE:
A CASE OF THE MONDAYS

IN CASE YOU'RE STILL WONDERING, MOST OF THE KIDS AT WOOD INTERMEDIATE STILL HATE ME...

But can you blame them? I totally WRECKED their science fair projects. Okay, hold up... for those of you just joining our regularly scheduled program, let me fill you in on the deets.

Previously, on Kid Youtuber... I tried starting the most epic food fight the world had ever seen, but it backfired miserably because I was the only one who threw food. And the only thing I hit was the back of Dutch McKenzie's head.

Dutch is my own personal bully – a 10th grader stuck in 8th grade. You see, Dutch started kindergarten a year later than everyone else, and then he got held back in 4th grade for I don't even know what. So, that makes him 14 years old. A whole TWO years older than the oldest kids at Wood Intermediate.

He's the only 8th grader who drives himself to school.

Anyways, as payback for slapping a taco against his skull, he duct taped me to the wall for his science fair project, but not before I obliterated everybody else's projects trying to escape.

They call me the Science Fair Sabotager because of that.

And that's the story of why everybody hates me.

Okay, fine. Maybe kids don't HATE me, but they sure don't love me the way I had planned. You see, I was SUPPOSED to be a mega YouTube star by now. Money, fame, private jets? All would be mine if the universe just did what I told it to.

But that's not how it works. Instead, I'm still just a kid that disappears in a crowded hallway. That has to find an empty seat at lunch because nobody saves me a spot. That has to wait in line for the bathroom because I don't have my own private one yet.

But now that I have my camera back, I'm pumped about making videos again! My only problem is that I'm kind of out of ideas, so that's where my Fans come in!

If you've got an idea for a video, leave it in the comments and I'll do my best to make your idea come to life!

EPISODE FOUR:
CEREAL IS JUST BREAKFAST SOUP

So, check this out – RIGHT AFTER I uploaded yesterday's video, I IMMEDIATELY got a comment under it, like, BAM! It was from my friend Emma! I mean, it was from CoolDad81.

Wink wink.

Challenge accepted!

Sort of.

You see, after a little bit of research, I found out that the world's biggest Rice Crispy treat was 2,400 pounds. It was made from 800 pounds of Rice Crispies and 1,400 pounds of marshmallows.

That thing was, like, the size of my bedroom!

That world record was too big for me to break.

But what I COULD do was try to make the TOWN'S biggest Rice Crispy treat. That was easy. The record for that was set in 1962 by Old Man Garrick – the retired teacher who runs detention at Wood Intermediate.

ALLS I DID WAS MAKE A TRIPLE BATCH WITH THREE BOXES. NEVER INTENDED ON BREAKING NO RECORDS.

So, to break the town record for biggest Rice Crispy treat, all I had to do was make mine with FOUR boxes?

Pssh! Easy! TOO easy, actually!

I'm Davy Spencer, future YouTube rockstar, and I don't do little things. I'm all about the "GO BIG OR GO HOME" lifestyle, so I decided to make a Rice Crispy treat with TWENTY boxes instead!

I was a little worried that my mom would kill the project when I asked her to buy me twenty boxes of cereal, but once I told her it was for school, she was pretty cool with it.

YOU SAY YOU NEED THIS FOR SCHOOL?

UH, YEAH, FOR SOCIAL STUDIES!

Technically, that's not a lie. I'm doing it so kids at my SCHOOL will think I'm cool. As far as the social studies part? I mean, how is this NOT a study in social behavior?

I KNOW WHAT DAVY'S UP TO, BUT HE'S HAVING A HARD TIME BEING THE NEW KID. I'D BUY HIM A THOUSAND BOXES IF IT HELPS HIM DEAL WITH THOSE EMOTIONS.

After we got all the ingredients, Chuck, Annie, and me went straight to work making the largest Rice Crispy treat this town had ever seen!

It was gonna be so huge that people in town were gonna be like, "Whoa, that's so huge!" and they'd tell their friends, who'd tell their friends, who'd tell their friends until everybody on the PLANET heard about it!

At least, THAT was the plan.

First, we had to mix all the ingredients together, but that's way easier said than done when you're talking about twenty boxes of cereal. It's not like I had a GIGANTIC MASSIVE bowl sitting around somewhere.

But what I DID have... was a bathtub.

It was a little grimy, sure, but after a quick rinse, it was restaurant-level clean, so we poured all twenty boxes of cereal straight into the tub.

21

The longest part was microwaving the butter and marshmallows. That took forever. We had BAGS and BAGS and BAGS of marshmallows and TONS of butter that needed to be melted together.

Chuck and Annie brought microwaves with them, so while they were nuking marshmallows, I was running back and forth between the kitchen and the bathroom to mix everything while it was still hot.

But all that melting was easy compared to mixing everything together. We tried using wooden spoons, but those only lasted about thirty seconds before they snapped. It was like trying to stir cement!

Without anything to stir the Rice Crispy mix, we were sort of stuck. But not for long because, lucky for us, I suddenly had a GENIUS idea, y'know, like I often do.

I ran back to my room as fast I could to change my clothes, and when I got back, Annie and Chuck knew exactly what I was thinking...

But I totally did.

I dove right into the bathtub.

Well, more like, sunk slowly into it.

Look, the way I saw it – we could've bailed on the whole project and wasted all that food, or I could've taken one for the team by getting into the tub and massaging the melted marshmallows together with the Rice Crispies.

I'm pretty sure I made the right decision.

After everything was mixed up, I let it sit in the bathtub overnight because it needed to set. "Setting" means letting it get firm because who likes a Rice Crispy treat that falls apart in their fingers?

Psychos. That's who.

When I got up the next morning, my gigantic bathtub

dessert was finished. It was even more perfect than I ever could've imagined, glistening like some kind of priceless alien geode.

Chuck came by before school and helped me hoist it out of the tub. It took a while, and a ton of wiggling it back and forth, but it finally came out with a PLOP!

After that, we put it on my sister's little red wagon and headed off to school.

Annie and Fergus were waiting out front. Normally, I'm not into the idea of Fergus tagging along with us to school (like he's done every day since we moved next door to him), but today was different. Today was gonna be awesome, I could feel it. It was something in the air. So, having Fergus rocking along with us wasn't a big deal to me.

Plus, Fergus could pull the Rice Crispy treat behind his wheelchair super easily.

I hopped up and hung on to the Rice Crispy treat like I was George Washington crossing the DeLorean River or whatever it's called.

Aaaaaand, I don't want to toot my own horn – wait, what am I talking about? Tooting my own horn is the whole point of my channel! The second we got to school, kids were waiting, practically cheering for Rice Crispy treats. It was like they knew we were coming!

And Emma was right there with them.

I gotta be honest here... I was NOT expecting that.

Most of my plans end up backfiring spectacularly, so it was a nice change of pace to have things go my way.

I'm pretty sure Emma had something to do with the warm welcome since she was the one who suggested the Rice Crispy treat in the first place.

Annie and Chuck ripped pieces off the Rice Crispy brick while Fergus and I handed them out to kids for free. Even some of the teachers got in on that action.

We were having so much fun out there that we completely lost track of time. There were still a dozen kids outside when the bell rang! Everybody ran off at the same time.

Just before I made it to homeroom, I got stopped in the hallway by Chad Schulte, one of the hall monitors. There was another kid with him that I'd never seen at school before – a hall monitor in training or something.

The rookie's name was Parker, and I was positive that he was gonna write me up for being tardy. Rookies tend to do that sort of thing, y'know, because they're trying to impress the higher ups.

Anyways, I was already on thin ice with Principal Hawkins because of the whole science fair thing, and I didn't need to give him another reason to think I was a bad egg!

So, I started pleading with Parker to let me off the hook, but he stopped me from finishing. He held his hand up, smiled, and then he said...

Parker and Chad weren't there to bust me! They were there because they heard about my Rice Crispy treat! The word had spread around the school so fast!

And of course, I gave them some because I'm cool like that. They said "Thanks!" and let me head to homeroom.

I slipped into class like a slithering ninja and found an empty seat near the back. My homeroom teacher, Miss Jacky, never even saw me sneak in, I'm that good.

I mean, it wasn't really hard since she was working on her laptop while Principal Hawkins' voice blared over the intercom for morning announcements.

Everybody in the room went silent when Hawkins said the thing about the bike. I think we were all surprised at how cool the prize was. Most of the time, middle-school prizes are coupons for a free personal pizza or an extra small ice cream cone.

Prizes are never anything like a BIKE.

As soon as homeroom ended, kids were out the door, racing to catch a glimpse of the prize in the lobby, myself included.

I've never seen anything so beautiful in my entire life.

EPISODE FIVE:
I WHEELIE LIKE BIKES

That thing is seriously tricked out with 100% chromium molybdenum steel (aka — chromoly), double-butted main frame, integrated head tube, integrated seat clamp, machined mid-bottom bracket, micro dropouts, removeable cable guides and brake mounts...

I don't know what ANY of that means, but it SOUNDS good.

No wonder kids in school were drooling over it. More specifically, DUTCH was drooling over it. He was already in the lobby when I got there, staring at the bike and breathing heavily. Pretty sure a tear rolled down his cheek, too.

I never took Dutch as a BMX biker, but I guess that's why they say, "Never judge a book by its cover."

Dutch had a camera aimed at the bike, doing some voice-over for — oh, right — you don't know yet!

31

Dutch McKenzie started his own YouTube channel!

I'm not saying the dude's totally trying to rip me off, but he's totally trying to rip me off. He started vlogging the night of the science fair. His first video was of his science fair project – my body versus duct tape.

PREVIOUSLY ON Kid YouTuber...

He got a C+ for it.

The other videos he's been uploading aren't as exciting, though. That happens to a lot of YouTubers, y'know – they start strong and fizzle out because they run outta ideas.

He mostly films himself reviewing food that he microwaved. Wait.

Hold on because this is important.

I didn't say "microwaved food." I said "food he microwaved."

So, he never reviews TV dinners or popcorn or anything you're SUPPOSED to cook in a microwave. Nope, he reviews random food that he thinks might be good if they were warmed up.

Yup.

That's seriously all he does, and he's uploaded over a hundred videos already! Over ONE HUNDRED VIDEOS of himself horking down food he microwaved!

The most frustrating part about it is that he's got MORE Fans than I do! I mean, just look at his Fan count! TWENTY Fans! The dude's a star, and all he does is eat questionable food!

I'm not gonna lie – when I saw that he got more Fans than me, I tried following his lead.

Also, for future reference – I don't recommend microwaving sushi. Everything we cook in our microwave tastes fishy now.

EPISODE SIX:
JUMP TO CONCLUSIONS

I'VE DISCOVERED MY TRUE CALLING...

26 VIEWS   9 FANS

So, by lunchtime, I was still a pretty popular guy in the school. A lot of kids were giving me high-fives and fist-bumps for the free snacks I brought that morning, which was pretty awesome, and wait... I worry that what you just heard me say was that the high-fives and fist-bumps were pretty awesome.

No, I'm talking about what I did.

Me giving out free treats. That was pretty awesome. You get it.

Anyways, high-fives are all good, don't get me wrong, but I still had a LONG way to go to win everybody over. Wood Intermediate kids really know how to hold a grudge.

If there was an Olympic event for holding onto negative feelings, kids at this school would take 1st, 2nd, AND 3rd place.

Chuck, Annie, and I found three empty spots at a table in the back of the cafeteria — three spots that Fergus was saving for us. And he always gives me the seat next to him.

I don't know why he automatically assumes I'll sit with him. I mean, yeah, I've sat with him every single day for the past two weeks, but that's only because I'm trying to siphon some of his Fans over to my channel.

Sometimes he makes videos during lunch. And sometimes I weasel my way into the back of those videos. It's not personal. It's just business.

When lunch was almost over, Emma showed up, still nibbling on her Rice Crispy treat. She was trying to make it last the whole school day.

Then she told me it was super cool that I made a whole video based on her suggestion and said other kids must've thought the same thing because she noticed that my Fan count went up.

Fergus busted out his laptop and checked the numbers, and yes, as a matter of fact, my Fan count DID go up. By TEN.

Look, ten may not be a big number for some people, but to me, it's HUGE. If I got TEN new Fans a day, I'd have ONE HUNDRED THOUSAND new Fans in a year!

The only problem is – I don't know how to get ten new Fans a day. I've tried everything, but none of it seemed to work.

Okay, I haven't tried EVERYTHING, but I've tried a lot of things, which is closer to trying EVERYTHING than trying NOTHING.

And then, Emma said...

Honestly, it wasn't a bad idea. A lot of vloggers do that, but does it ever work? I mean, yeah, it worked for me once, but I doubt it would work again.

I dunno. Emma and my friends were all waiting for me to say something, so I figured it wouldn't hurt to try.

Fergus let me use his camera to make a quick video right there in the lunchroom.

Then we uploaded it with Fergus' laptop, and guess what happened. In less than 30 seconds, I got a reply!

TheOneAndOnly 2 seconds ago

jump the gully in your backyard on a bike :)

It was crazy to get a reply THAT fast, but what's even crazier is that the person who made it told me to jump the gully!

That meant they were watching my other videos, too!

That was SUCH a good sign that things could be headed in the right direction for me! And by "the right direction," I mean becoming "super-duper uber famous."

Then Fergus' laptop dinged again.

And again.

And again.

DING! 😊 **DinoDr** 4 seconds ago

yes jump teh gully!!1

DING! 😊 **foreverskyler11** 3 seconds ago

Jump the freaking gully already!

DING! 😊 **Forrester09c98** 2 seconds ago

you better jump the gully or i'll unFan you!

Four comments in under a minute?

Boom! Four comments was a big deal! Four comments was the start of a million comments! But I didn't want to get too excited. Not yet. I knew I needed to remain calm – to give it more time, but then... the dings started POURING in.

It was amazing. Motivating. Inspiring. It was the most interaction I had ever gotten on ANY of my videos, and it was all thanks to Emma's suggestion for suggestions.

Fans wanted me to jump the gully with a bike. The only problem was... I didn't have a bike!

Before my family moved here, we had a "get-rid-of-all-our-

40

stuff" garage sale so we wouldn't have as much to pack.

My bike was one of the first things that sold. Got five bucks for it. Looking back, I prob'ly could'a got more.

Anyways, without a bike, how could I even consider making a video of myself jumping the gully.

There was no way I'd clear that sucker on foot, and I seriously doubted that my dad would let me drive our car for something like that... but it never hurts to ask.

I'd use Krissy's bike if she had one, but the only thing she's riding around is a little plastic car.

You know the kind – the red and yellow ones that every little kid in the world has and every single garage sale sells. It's like the Toyota Corolla of kid's toy cars.

But the dings kept coming on my video, so I had to think of something, anything! Those were new Fans that I didn't wanna let down!

New Fans that I wanted to keep! If I asked for suggestions and failed to deliver, they'd unFan me faster than you can say whatever you can say really fast!

Babies with the buggy bumpers or Sally with the seashells thing, I don't know!

Then it hit me – an idea so perfect that I almost couldn't believe it.

My problem was that I needed to jump the gully in my backyard, but I don't own a bike.

And the solution to that problem was sitting in the front lobby of the school in all its shiny chromium molybdenum glory. And right at that moment, I knew exactly what I had to do...

EPISODE SEVEN:
IT'S HAPPENING

FRIDAY.
AFTER SCHOOL.
I'M JUMPIN'
THE GULLY.

TELL YOUR
FRIENDS.

26 VIEWS   9 FANS

But first, I needed to win the BMX bike that was sitting in the lobby of Wood Intermediate. Funny how God works, sometimes, right? It's, like, He knew I wanted to be famous, so He put the gully in my backyard and told me where to find the bike.

HEY, WHERE YOU GUYS GOIN'?

OVER HERE. I DON'T WANNA BE NEAR YOU WHEN YOU GET STRUCK BY LIGHTNING.

45

Winning the bike from the Help the Hungry food drive means that I had to bring the most canned goods by the end of the week.

There was gonna be a TON of kids trying to do the same thing, so I've got my work cut out for me. I already tore through our pantry at home to find cans, but we barely had anything since we just moved in. All I found were two cans of baked beans.

Chuck brought me six cans of mushrooms from his parent's motel, and Annie's parents only allowed her to give me one can of peas. I mean, can you believe that?

It's for a good cause, Mr. and Mrs. Yun!

That brought my grand total to NINE cans. That was a decent start, but if I wanted even a CHANCE of winning that bike, I was gonna need WAY more than NINE flippin' cans. It hadn't even been twenty-four hours, and Dutch was already beating me.

How do I know?

Because he was doing the exact same thing as me – making videos about his progress!

Can you FLIPPIN' believe that??

Dutch already had TWELVE cans of those little baby hot dogs, and that was without even trying! Winning that bike was gonna be harder than I thought. It was time to up my game. Think outside the box. Play for keeps, y'know?

So, I put on my best clothes and hit the streets with Chuck, Annie, and my sister's red wagon. It was still sticky from the Rice Crispy brick, but I just threw a sheet over all that. Problem solved. And I just wanna say – I looked totally profesh. Like I was on my way to a job interview for becoming a billionaire.

The first few houses we hit were duds. Nobody even answered their doors. But I bet they were home because they all had those doorbell cameras.

You know, the ones that are like, "Motion detected at the front door," whenever anything moves outside. Then, when you ring the bell, a little camera turns on so people can spy on whoever's outside their house.

Sometimes they talk to you through the microphone, and it makes you feel like you're living in the future or something.

Most of the time, they just watch silently, acting like they're not home, but it's all lies.

At the end of the block, Fergus caught up to us, excited to help. Even though he was my next-door neighbor, I skipped his house because I figured he'd want to join us on our can collecting quest. I was right.

We went a few more blocks, hitting up every house on every street, but in the end only picked up about three cans total. I say "about three cans" because one dude gave us an open can of creamed corn he was in the middle of eating.

Pretty sure "leftovers" won't count as donations. Maybe they'd take it if I put some plastic over the top.

It's hard not to feel defeated after so many rejections. I don't know. Maybe we should've tried a different neighborhood. I think the problem was that my face was too familiar to all the houses we went to.

After that, we gave up on the houses, but not the dream.

Besides, people in those houses were just the MIDDLEMEN to kids looking for cans.

If I wanted to take donations like the big boys, I was gonna have to go to the source...

Grocery stores donate stuff all the time, everybody knows that, so I was a little surprised that nobody else from school had come up with that idea before me.

Well, that's not true. I'm not actually surprised.

Now that I think of it, it's no wonder I thought of it first since I've probably got the biggest brains at Wood Intermediate.

...that's right, isn't it?

Big brains means big smarts?

I'm gonna go with "Yes" on that.

Anyways, getting a face-to-face with the manager wasn't hard, especially cuz I was already wearing a suit. All I did was waltz into his office like a boss and state my business.

After a little bit of schmoozing (AKA pestering), I got exactly what I wanted.

He said he'd be happy to donate because I was a sharp-looking kid and because it was for a good cause.

500 pounds of peanut butter!

I know peanut butter doesn't normally come in cans, but he said this one did, so it counts as a canned good!

I'd probably win the bike with just THAT donation!

Then he had us wait outside while somebody went and fetched it. And while we were out there, we spotted Dutch standing at the far end of the grocery store parking lot with a whole WHEELBARROW full of cans.

He waved when he saw us, but it was a sarcastic wave.

Then I noticed the sign in the hands.

That sneaky jerk-face was playing unfair!

Pulling on the heartstrings of compassionate people like that?

NOT COOL, dude!

I marched right up and called him out on it.

Ugh!

He wasn't wrong, but STILL.

At least Dutch gave up after that. He dumped all his cans into the trunk of his car, and then peeled out of the parking lot blaring some '80s metal.

Pretty sure Dutch only has a permit to drive to school, so

I'll let YOU figure out the legal implications on that one.

When the dust cleared and the smell of burnt rubber disappeared, an employee from Foodalicious met us outside with the peanut butter they were donating.

That turned out to be an epic headache on a whole different level.

Yes, the peanut butter was for real.

There was 500 pounds of it, and it was technically canned.

I kindly refused the oil drum of peanut butter, and then we hiked it back to my place totally drained. We had spent the last two hours working our butts off just to get TWO AND A HALF cans of food?

Back at my place, my mom made us buttered toast and chocolate milk that we were all digging into. Sometimes the simplest foods are the best ones.

Then, out of nowhere, Fergus said...

YOU SHOULD ASK YOUR FANS TO HELP YOU WIN THE BIKE!

Yeah, right, like anybody would do that.

Why the heck would random people on the internet help me?

How would that even work? Would they email me a canned good? As cool and sci-fi as that sounds, it's impossible... I think. Maybe modern-day science has figured it out, but there was no way that kind of technology was available to a pleb like me.

REAL mail could work, but I think that starts to cost money after a certain weight, and last I check, metal cans filled with food are HEAVY AS HECK.

I said all that to Fergus, but he didn't stop. He was like some kind of "advice giving" machine cranked to eleven. He started machine-gunning ideas like crazy – it's something he said he does when he's trying to come up with videos – he says it's easier to find a good idea in a pile of bad ones.

Personally, I think throwing out bad ideas is a waste of time. Why not just try to come up with a BUNCH of good ideas instead?

Finally, Fergus blurted out an idea so bad that it made us all stop in our tracks.

It wasn't the WORST plan I ever heard, but...

Why would anybody leave a can at my locker when they could just donate it themselves to try to win the bike?

I didn't feel like arguing, so I rolled with Fergus' dumb idea, fully knowing it wasn't gonna go anywhere. He helped me make a short video asking my Fans for help, and that was that – the end of the night.

He worked a bit of his editing magic. Added music. Uploaded it to YouTube. And then he made it live.

It was almost embarrassing because I knew nobody would do something stupid like leave a can at my locker. I was a hundred percent positive that was something that would NEVER, EVER happen.

Never in a MILLION, BILLION years.

So when I got to school the next morning and saw a canned good sitting under my locker... I was blown away.

EPISODE EIGHT:
MILKY MILK MILKERSON

I'm not a huge fan of milk unless it's chocolate.

Or strawberry.

Or banana.

Or even almond as long as it's the vanilla flavored one.

But that's fine! I'd drink regular milk because one of my Fans asked me to do it!

I got super pumped about it. Just the fact that Fergus' idea worked! Wow! Y'know, that kid MIGHT actually know what he's talking about when it comes to making videos. I'll admit that. Maybe he can even teach me a thing or two.

See what I did there? That's called being humble, and I'm the most humble guy I know.

All morning I'd been prepping for the big event that was

going down at lunch, sucking in huge breaths, holding them, then releasing them slowly.

YOU KNOW YOU'RE NOT GONNA STORE THE MILK IN YOUR LUNGS, RIGHT?

Since there aren't any gallon-sized milk jugs in the school, I'd have to make it work using milk cartons. Annie did the math. Milk cartons contain a half pint of milk each, and since one gallon is eight pints, I'd need to drink...

24 MILK CARTONS??

CLOSE. YOU NEED 16 CARTONS.

MATH IS HARD, BUDDY.

When I got to the lunchroom, I half-expected a crowd of kids waiting for me, but there wasn't one. It's cool, though! Becoming a star comes AFTER a video goes viral. And this video was gonna be the viralest!

Instead of buying lunch, I spent all my money on buying milk cartons. I figured I probably needed to save room in my stomach, and food would just get in the way.

I also chose to run with SKIM milk since 1% was heavier. Skim milk is basically diet milk.

But when I got to the register, I found out I could only afford four milks. I still needed twelve more! Chuck and Fergus both gave me theirs, which brought me up to six, but Annie refused to give me hers.

Annie went to ask other students if I could have their milk. Chuck, Fergus, and me found a place to sit in the cafeteria. Somewhere right in the middle of all the action, but not too crowded or else nobody would be able to see me do the thing.

Fergus set up a camera. I took a seat, cracked my knuckles, and tore open the little triangle on the top of carton number one. Then, I chugged the whole thing, no problem.

This challenge was gonna be a breeze.

Fergus held up a sign he made with #1 on it – he made one for each carton of milk I was gonna drink so we could keep track without having to count out loud. He's forward-thinking like that.

Chuck started cheering for me, which got the attention of other students in the lunchroom. A few of them even came over, and after Chuck explained what was going on, they gave me their milks!

I didn't wanna leave my new Fans waiting, so I tore open another box and went to chug-town, population ME.

Not gonna lie.

That second box was a little harder than the first, but nobody said it would be easy. They only said it would be worth it.

Well, nobody said it'd be worth it, either.

But I was really starting to hope it was worth it, because my stomach was already feeling pretty tight, even AFTER all that heavy breathing I'd done!

Two boxes down. Fourteen more to go.

I slammed a third box to the sounds of screaming children. It was tough, but those kids out there? They gave me strength. They were the real heroes.

I'd never felt so alive in my life, but at the same time, I'd never felt so gross. THREE boxes of milk were sloshing around my insides – I could actually HEAR liquid splash when I jiggled my belly!

Thirteen boxes left.

That's when Annie returned with a single milk carton. I was a little annoyed because we still needed a bunch of milk, and all she could find was ONE stinkin' box of the stuff?

It's almost like she didn't even try! Whatever.

I grabbed it and downed it.

Four in my belly.

More kids gathered around me, and we reached our goal of 16 milk boxes easily with their generosity.

Hooray...

I stared at the unopened milks in front of me, trying to figure out how to make this work, but my brain was getting foggy. My stomach hurt. Everything was blurry.

But I had a video to make. A Fan asked for this, and there was no way I was gonna let that person down. If I didn't go through with it, I'd risk losing that person as a Fan, and at this stage of my YouTube game, I needed every Fan I could get!

Chuck suggested I drink the rest as fast as possible. Fergus agreed. The longer I waited, the worse I was gonna feel, so they thought I should just get the whole thing over with.

I didn't even think about it. I grabbed another two boxes, tore the tops off and poured them down my throat.

Six milks in my stomach – ten more in front of me.

Keep.

Moving.

Forward.

That was all I could think. I grabbed the seventh milk carton, my hand shaking, milk dripping from my chin. My shirt was soaked. I didn't know if it was milk or sweat or some kind of gross hybrid milk-sweat. Was it possible that milk was coming out of my glands?

I'm no scientist, but... maybe?

I slowly brought the box to my lips. When I opened my mouth, it made a nasty "SPLORCH" sound. The waxy cardboard touched my bottom lip, making my throat flinch, and that was it.

I honked all over myself. All over the lunch table. All over the floor. Kids dove out of the way as every last drop of milk came roaring out of my mouth with a vengeance.

If I could've stopped, I would've, but I was having an out-of-body experience, watching the nightmare take place like I was just another student in the cafeteria.

Finally, after what felt like forever, I was finished.

It was awful, and the floor was white with milk. Some kids

were in shock; others had slipped and fallen in my milk puddle.

The gym teacher, Miss Gymalski, took me to the boy's locker room and let me hose myself off while she went and got some extra clothes for me from the school shop. Remember her? She's the Olympic weightlifter from Austria that retired and became a gym teacher at Wood.

As I walked back to my locker alone, I was bummed. Failing the milk challenge meant that I was letting down the kid who left me that suggestion.

It meant that I'd probably lose that person as a Fan.

It meant I'd probably lose a BUNCH of Fans, actually, because who would wanna watch my channel after all that?

Well, apparently, SOME kids did, because when I got back to my locker... there were three more cans waiting for me with slips of paper taped to each one.

EPISODE NINE:
YOU'LL NEVER BELIEVE WHAT I FOUND IN MY ATTIC

Kids were digging the can-challenge idea so much! My views were up, and I'd already got 34 Fans! It was a good thing I had the wisdom to take Fergus' advice, wasn't it?

That put me at 15 cans, and Dutch at...

Dutch was still beating me. Oh well. Can't focus on the negative; only on the positive, which was that I had three more cans at my locker, and three more suggestions!

First on the list: Tie helium balloons to a lawn chair until you fly away.

Easy enough. Chuck's dad uses balloons to advertise vacant rooms at their motel all the time, so getting as many as we needed wasn't a problem! His dad even HELPED us with it because he was curious to see if it would work.

Mr. Metropolis filled a balloon with helium and handed it to Annie, who handed it to Fergus, who handed it to Chuck, who then tied it to the lawn chair I was sitting on.

We did that for about an hour without any progress. 150 balloons tied to the chair, and I didn't even budge! Mr. Metropolis actually ran out of balloons, which meant he needed to make a trip to the store to buy more.

But during our break, I made the mistake of getting up from the chair to use the bathroom. The second my butt left the seat, the whole thing took off. Apparently 150 balloons wasn't enough to send a human into orbit, but it was enough to shoot a chair up there.

I hopped onto Chuck's shoulders and tried to grab the chair before it was too high, but that was a total fail.

BECAUSE DAVY'S A LOT HEAVIER THAN HE THINKS.

In the end, Chuck, Annie, Fergus, and I just watched the chair silently float away. Some say it's still in the sky today, watching over the town like a watchful protector.

GOODBYE, SWEET CHAIR...

CAN YOU GET OFF ME NOW? YOU WEIGH A TON.

The second video suggestion was for me to eat one ghost pepper! Just in case you don't know, the ghost pepper is one of the hottest peppers in the WORLD, topping over 1 MILLION Scoville Heat Units or something. You know it's the real deal when they get all sciency about it.

I was a little worried about being able to find a ghost pepper because our town isn't that big, so exotic menu items like that are hard to find.

But it turns out Foodalicious had them in stock!

After I bought a dried-up ghost pepper, we sat in the parking lot outside the grocery store and starting recording.

They say you're supposed to drink milk when you eat something hot, but after my milk challenge, I never wanted to see another glass of that stuff for as long as I lived, so I went with good ol' fashioned water instead.

Instead of tossing the whole pepper into my mouth and killing it in one bite, I went with a more mature direction by taking the teensiest, tinsiest bite off the end of it.

And you know what?

It wasn't bad.

It was actually kinda tasty. It had, like, a sweet chili flavor that reminded me of Thai food. Ghost peppers are supposed to be unbearably hot, but maybe they affect some people less than others?

I mean, it was spicy, but not THAT spicy.

I wouldn't be surprised if my body was naturally immune to them. I'm kind of talented in a bunch of unfamiliar ways, so having an insanely strong tolerance to spicy food makes perfect sense.

So, I threw the rest of the pepper into my mouth and started chomping away like a clueless cow.

Exactly 30 seconds later is when it hit me - the most intense burning I'd ever felt in my entire life.

How can I explain it? It's, like... if somebody took the sun... and put it inside my mouth... and then punched me in the face with another sun... and then another sun... sun sun... sun... the sun...

And it's funny how FOMO works, isn't it? Chuck and Fergus were watching me literally hallucinate on the ground, but for some reason, they both wanted to try a ghost pepper, too.

Chuck ran inside Foodalicious, bought two more peppers, came back out and gave one to Fergus.

Together, they took bites at the same time. I tried to warn them not to do it – that it wasn't worth the pain – but I was too busy losing myself to the infinite cosmos.

It was an hour before I could feel my tongue again.

So, that made two out of three videos done. Only one more to go, and I saved the worst-I mean BEST for last.

The final suggestion was for me to EXPLORE MY HAUNTED ATTIC.

Pretty cool, right?

That's just another example of Fans watching my OTHER videos, and not just the new ones! That meant that people would watch my new stuff, then click around my channel to find my older stuff because they liked what they saw!

They could lose themselves down the Davy rabbit hole!

When the four of us got back to my place, Fergus went next door to his house to grab some stuff he said he needed. I don't know what. I wasn't really listening. I was too distracted by the scary video I was about to make.

Something you might not know about me — I'm MASSIVELY afraid of the dark. I know, I know. How's that even possible? I'm such a stud in all the other parts of my life that it's redic to think that the dark would terrify me to my core!

Well, it's true.

The dark is my only weakness.

My kryptonite, if you will, so while Chuck was gearing up and Annie was talking to my sister, I was having a mild panic attack.

It was 8:30 pm, so the sun had gone down. The sky was black. The moon was out. And my attic was just... up there... being all creepy and ominous and stuff.

Chuck pulled down the ladder and waited for me to go first.

That's when Fergus returned almost like he was waiting for the perfect time to make his entrance. And when he showed up, he didn't have his wheelchair with him.

He was on his FEET.

Fergus can walk if he needs to?! I don't know why, but that made me really happy. I can't really explain why, though. Like, I felt happy... for somebody else? Weird, right?

Since it was my house, I had to go first, that's what Annie, Chuck, and Fergus decided. If it were up to me, I would've just thrown a camera and a flashlight up there and called it a night.

But I had a job to do. Fans to make happy. So, step by step, I went up the ladder and into the terrifying attic. Fergus was behind me, but Chuck and Annie weren't so fast to follow.

It was hot.

Not as hot as the ghost pepper, but still hot.

Muggy, too, kind of like a sauna with the lights out. I turned to call down the ladder, but that's when Annie decided it'd be hilarious if she slammed the hatch door behind me and Fergus.

It was pitch black in there.

As black as pitch.

Whatever pitch is.

Suddenly, the hatch door fell open and I tumbled right out.

I wish I could say my landing was graceful, but it wasn't. My undies snagged on a nail and I was stuck dangling in front of everybody as the ghost of the attic came closer and closer.

I was screaming my butt off. Some kind of paranormal monster was right behind me saying it wanted to eat my soul with ketchup and mustard, and it probably already ate Fergus' soul, but Annie and Chuck weren't even scared!

Actually, they were LAUGHING.

Then I saw the "ghost" as it came into the light, which was when I realized it was less of a "ghost" and more of a "little sister."

Annie gave Krissy a heads-up that I was filming in the attic, so my sister used it as an opportunity to prank me.

Ugh.

EPISODE TEN:
HAPPY WEDNESDAY

SIXTEEN MORE CANS AND SUGGESTIONS BY MY LOCKER THIS MORNING!

112 VIEWS   82 FANS

For any of you keeping score, I'm up to 31 cans. That's good, but not great. Those were still rookie numbers compared to Dutch, who's up to 62 already! He's kinda killin' it on the can collecting front, but only because he was using a different collection technique than anybody else.

GIVE ME YOUR CANNED GOODS SO I CAN DONATE THEM TO THE HUNGRY!

I'm pretty sure that "bullying for a good cause" isn't a real thing.

Kids at school had started talking about my stunt on Friday. Some of them even made t-shirts in their art class with the words, "JUMP THE GULLY!" on the front.

So, yeah, I'm kind of becoming the big deal I wanted to be. Even Principal Hawkins got onboard with what I was doing, like whaaaat? You'd think he'd be all "adult" about it and tell me I'm being irresponsible or something lame like that, but he TOTALLY wasn't! He was all for it!

Hawkins was so supportive of what I'm doing that he even left a can with a suggestion by my locker! And, I mean, he's the PRINCIPAL, so he got first dibs. His idea wasn't even that bad – it was actually pretty awesome. He wanted me to join as many Wood Intermediate clubs as I could THAT SCHOOL DAY!

Lemme explain – Wood's got about a hundred different clubs in it. Every day of the week, a different club meets during a different period. So, like, the Video Gaming Club meets during first period every Monday. Aggressive Knitting meets during second period every Monday, and blah blah blah.

Since it was Wednesday, I was only able to choose Wednesday clubs. And because this was Principal Hawkins' idea, I got to fill my entire day with clubs, which meant I GOT TO SKIP EVERY SINGLE CLASS LIKE A BOSS, BOOM!

FIRST PERIOD ON WEDNESDAY, AND I'M ABOUT TO KICK TUSHIE IN THE BRAZILIAN JIU-JITSU CLUB!

127 VIEWS   99 FANS

Chuck's the kid in charge of Brazilian Jiu-Jitsu. Does that surprise you, though? I mean, in his spare time, he runs around in ninja clothes, kicking trees for practice. Being in charge of Jiu-Jitsu makes perfect sense for him.

Once I got to the club, Chuck helped me find a gi that was my size. I said we could skip all that since I was only gonna be at one meeting, but he said it was mandatory.

Then I asked if I should wear any protective gear in case I got punched or something. He said no because there's not a lot of hitting in jiu-jitsu.

Weird, right?

I thought martial arts was all about Hurricane Kicks and Hundred Hand Slaps, but maybe that's just Street Fighter.

So, after some light stretching, Chuck had me come to the

front of the class so he could demonstrate some sweet moves for his students. At least, he SAID it was for his students. I think he was just showing off for the camera. The only instructions he gave me was to tap the ground if I was in pain.

Let me just say... Chuck's one of my best friends. He's a great guy, seriously, one of the best. But in that room, in front of all those kids... he was kind of a wad.

He knocked the wind right out of me. Didn't even give me a chance to recover before putting me in a lock.

Then he did it again...

And again...

And again...

Then he TRIED to do it again, but I was too quick for him that time. I squiggled out of his grip and quit the club right after that.

Brazilian Jiu-Jitsu is def not for me.

EPISODE TWELVE:
FANCY PANTS

THE FANCY PANTS CLUB IS THE PREMIER CLUB OF WOOD INTERMEDIATE SCHOOL...

132 VIEWS

112 FANS

Students were dressed like rich kids on the Titanic while waiters walked around with serving trays and everybody talked like they're from the 1920's.

BLIMEY! WHO'S THE HOOLIGAN THAT LACKS **FANCY PANTS**?

UH, IF YOU MEAN ME, THEN MY NAME'S DAVY.

Also, FYI – the Fancy Pants Club charges a monthly fee of $20 to pay for all the food and drinks they give to their members. On the menu today were tiny sandwiches – turkey and provolone on gluten-free bread cut into little triangles with a dollop of garlic aioli on each one.

I don't know, they were alright, I guess. I just felt like the bread was missing something...

After some mingling, everybody headed outside for a round of golf and a spot of tea.

I gotta say – golf is way easier than I expected. I was knocking balls out of the park, feeling pretty good about myself. That is, until somebody told me I was doing it wrong.

Overall, I give the Fancy Pants Club ONE star, but only because they told me if I didn't give them FIVE stars, I'd never be allowed to come back.

No bigs.

I'm pretty laid-back, so I just laughed it off, which only made them angrier.

I will NOT be visiting the Fancy Pants Club again any time soon.

EPISODE THIRTEEN:
FUTURE FARMERS

I FEEL LIKE I GOT LIED TO ON THIS ONE...

145 VIEWS   119 FANS

When I saw there was a "Future Farmers" club, I thought it would be FUTURISTIC farmers, like, with lasers and robots and stuff, but nope. It was just a club for kids interested in farming. Don't get me wrong, farmers are awesome! We need them, but I just... I really wanted to see some laser robots.

ARE THERE AT LEAST **SOME** LASERS?

NOPE!

Anyways, this club was off school property, so we had to take a bus to get there. Annie was in this club, too, which was nice to have somebody to sit with on the bus.

She wasn't really interested in the "farming" part, though.

UH, YEAH, BECAUSE WHERE ELSE CAN I PET A **COW?**

Since it was my first time at the farm, I got a special tour. It wasn't one of those MASSIVE farms like the ones you see when you're driving across the country. This farm was small. Like, SUPER small. They called it a "hobby farm," which meant they only did it for fun, and NOT for money, which made absolutely NO sense to me.

YOU MEAN YOU'RE DOING THAT BECAUSE YOU **WANT** TO?

One of the things I had to do was collect some chicken eggs. Everybody said the chickens were perfectly safe to be around, but I didn't believe it. One chicken kept eyeing me like it knew I was comin' for some eggs.

I should've trusted my gut. As soon as I grabbed an egg, that bird came at me like a freakin' rocket with feathers.

After that, I went back to the bus until we returned to school, but even there, that one chicken sat outside my window, mean-muggin' me.

No video is worth getting pecked by a psychotic chicken.

EPISODE FOURTEEN:
YOGA IS FOR POSERS

Okay, wait, the relaxation part was easy. I'm super good at that. It was the stretchy poses part I had trouble with. The club started as soon as I got there. Nobody said a word, not even the student leading the club. I guess being silent was part of it.

The first part was easy enough – just basically sit and stare at nothing while ocean sounds played in the background.

Then we did another pose, breathing and exhaling slowly. If this club was a video game, the first pose would've been level 1, and the second pose would've been level 2, harder, but not TOO much harder.

All I had to do was bend my body and raise my hand like I was waving.

Then we got to the third pose – level 3. That's when things got... complicated. This was where I couldn't really keep up anymore. I mean, I COULD'VE tried, but I was getting a headache just watching the other kids do it...

At level 4, I straight-up quit.

Who needs strong fingers anyways?

EPISODE FIFTEEN:
CLOWN CLUB

YEAAAAH... SO COULROPHOBIA IS A REAL THING. IT'S THE FEAR OF CLOWNS...

184 VIEWS

156 FANS

And now I have it.

NOPE.

EPISODE SIXTEEN:
SURVIVAL CLUB

SURVIVAL CLUB IS A CLUB FOR KIDS WHO WANT TO LEARN HOW TO SURVIVE IN THE WILD...

AND THERE'S ONLY ONE PERSON IN IT.

191 VIEWS   184 FANS

That one member's name is Aksel, and he's pretty hardcore about being in nature. When I got outside, he was already dressed in leaves and twigs and stuff. He looked like a walking shrubbery.

WHERE ARE YOUR CLOTHES?

THESE ARE MY CLOTHES.

Who was I to argue? I was there to learn how to survive being on a desert island, not to argue about fashion. I grabbed a handful of leaves and made myself a little crown.

Aksel got to work right away, showing me the collection of sticks that he had made from much larger sticks. Then he showed me how it was done by taking a big ol' stick... and breaking all the little branches off it until it was smaller, like, yeah.

After that, I was already feeling parched. You see, when you're out in the wild for long periods of time, you need to be careful not to get dehydrated.

Dehydration is the number one cause of being thirsty.

Aksel was a pro – he knew exactly where to find a source of clean water. But honestly, I probably would've found it, too, if you gave me enough time.

Then Aksel showed me how to forage for food, which was less "foraging" and more "finding a vending machine" inside the school.

I was starting to get the feeling that Aksel was full of bologna. All he did was wear a bunch of leaves and make sticks out of other sticks! So far, I hadn't learned ANYTHING about how to survive in the wild!

I quit the club right after he explained the toilet paper situation to me.

EPISODE SEVENTEEN:
BEST AND WORST BATHROOMS AT WOOD

OKAY, ENOUGH WITH THE CLUBS. TIME FOR SOME **ACTUALLY** IMPORTANT STUFF...

LIKE, WHICH BATHROOMS ARE **GOOD** AND WHICH ONES ARE **GROSS.**

222 VIEWS   199 FANS

Now that we're done with clubs, let's talk about something more important – bathrooms breaks. I went to every single bathroom at Wood in search of the best and worst ones, so you know which to avoid and which to visit!

Is "visit" the right word? Do you "visit" a bathroom?

This video was actually suggested by a bunch of different peeps! I guess you guys really wanna know where to go when ya gotta go.

To me, before I started this journey, a bathroom was a bathroom. But now that I've experienced true luxury, I can never go back.

Wood Intermediate has 15 different bathrooms that I know of, but not all of them are easy to find.

Some are hidden gems. Some are horror-level grossness. So,

let's get started!

Top 3 WORST restrooms at Wood! Avoid these at all costs!

Third worst – THE BOY'S LOCKER ROOM.

This one was easy. I'm pretty sure boy's locker rooms are universally disgusting. For starters, the toilets don't have stall doors.

Yup. ZERO privacy.

The stalls are like really short hallways with toilet bowls at the end of them. And if you're brave enough to use one, you'd better hope there's TP or else you're gonna be stuck, staring at an empty cardboard tube in humiliating silence.

Second worst – THE STORAGE CLOSET IN THE MAIN HALL.

This one's just weird. There's a gigantic closet in the main hallway that has all the school cleaning supplies in it – mops, brooms, towels, bleach, and other liquid stuff.

But there's also a toilet bowl in the middle of it.

It's just sitting in there like it got lost and gave up trying to find a home. The toilet works. It's got plumbing and flushes like normal.

But why is it there?

Did some janitor get fed up with having to WALK to a REAL bathroom or something?

First worst – THE TRACK AND FIELD OUTHOUSE.

Technically, this restroom's not even on school property, but I'm counting it because students use it sometimes.

Next to the track outside the gym, there's a rickety old outhouse that's been there since before the school was built. Like, a HUNDRED YEARS before the school was built.

You walk inside, and there's just a bench with a hole in it.

If you're brave enough to use this bathroom, there's a rope you're supposed to tie around your waist, y'know, JUST IN CASE YOU FALL IN. Nobody really knows how deep the hole goes. Some say it goes to the center of the Earth, but I'm not gonna test that theory.

It's so nasty that I can't even talk about it anymore.

Moving along to the TOP 3 BEST restrooms!

Third Best — THE ORCHESTRA ROOM.

Most of you probably didn't even know this one existed! Orchestra kids are really protective of these, which makes sense because they're big, barely used, and fully stocked with toilet paper. They've even got one of those space-aged NASA hand dryers that shoots air like a jet engine.

FSHHHHHHHHH!

Second best – THE WOMEN'S RESTROOM IN THE TEACHER'S LOUNGE.

Besides the obvious privacy of "no kids allowed," the women's room in the teacher's lounge has an extra room attached to it. There's, like, flowery wallpaper, a chandelier, a microwave, a fridge, and a giant couch where you can kick back and relax. It's even got a 42-inch TV with NETFLIX on it.

First Best – PRINCIPAL HAWKIN'S PERSONAL RESTROOM.

Principal Hawkins' very own bathroom ATTACHED to his office! Nobody else has access to this thing. The inside smells like autumn – pine trees and bonfire. It's got your typical toilet and sink, but since this bathroom is just for Hawkins, he's got his own stuff in it!

There's a toothbrush, toothpaste, mouthwash, extra dress shirts, a razor for shaving, hair gel, hair spray, a hair dryer, fingernail clippers, the works! So, if you're ever in need of ANY of that stuff, just go straight to the principal's office. It's all there, and I'm sure he'd be happy to share it.

EPISODE EIGHTEEN:
THE DEETS

TWO DAYS UNTIL THE JUMP! I FIGURED I'D TAKE A LOOK AT THE GULLY TO SEE EXACTLY WHAT I'M DEALING WITH...

252 VIEWS   207 FANS

I got a bunch more cans at my locker after school. They say that coming up with new content is hard, but not when I've got a billion people giving me ideas! I'll have enough to keep me busy even AFTER the hunger drive is over!

So far, I had 67 cans, but Dutch was still winning at 90 cans. He was still snatching them from other kids. Not sure why the Hall Monitors weren't doing anything about it.

BECAUSE WE'VE GOT **BIGGER** PROBLEMS THAN DUTCH TO WORRY ABOUT!

That's okay because I had two days to catch up. It might be close, but with everybody's help, I think I've got a chance at winning that bike!

After school today, Chuck, Annie, Fergus, and I went down to the gully to start prepping for the jump. It was a big deal, and I wanted to be ready for it.

My backyard is a slope that leads down to the gully, but riding a bike through all the bumpy grass was gonna slow me down. My family had cardboard boxes leftover from moving into our house, so Chuck flattened those out and taped them together to give me a smoother surface to ride down.

At the bottom of the hill was a pretty dope ramp we put together earlier.

Fergus was setting up some cinder blocks and logs that were left in our yard when we moved in. That's where my Fans were gonna sit and watch as I made history.

Annie took some measurements of the gully.

Annie even brought a watermelon to drop into the gully so we could get an idea of what would happen if I spilled over the side.

The results were... discouraging.

Everybody was quiet for a moment.

That's when their attitudes changed all of a sudden.

Chuck told me that maybe I shouldn't do the jump. Fergus and Annie agreed. And honestly, I was starting to wonder if it was a good idea, myself.

But I had to get that kind of thinking outta my head!

I was following my dream! On my way to becoming what I've

always wanted to be! It was happening, and I couldn't just bail on that now because things were getting scary!

It was the first time I'd actually thought about the death-defying stunt in a real way. Like, before all that, I was PUMPED because it just sounded so cool, but standing there, looking at the busted-up watermelon at the bottom of the gully...

I was getting nervous.

So were my friends.

But this was for the Fans, who are LIKE my friends, but faceless and on the internet!

Anyways, to take our minds off the jump and hopefully bring some joy back to the group, I grabbed another suggestion out of my backpack that was overflowing with those little slips of paper.

But that only made things worse.

The suggestion was so dumb. I didn't even read it out loud.

But Annie wouldn't take no for an answer. That just made Chuck and Fergus want to know what the paper said, too.

Annie didn't believe me because I was obviously lying. Chuck chased me down and started tickling me, which felt a little unnecessary and embarrassing, but whatever. Then Annie snatched the slip of paper out of my hand.

How could anybody suggest something like that? Why would somebody even give me a can for that? Was it for real? Was it a joke?

Fergus took a deep breath, and then he said...

Chuck and Annie left, too.

That dumb suggestion really killed the mood.

I don't get it. Like, are some people wads JUST to be wads? What's the point? The world would be a better place if everybody was just nice to each other.

How hard is it to do that??

And you know what else I don't get? Fergus has the most popular YouTube channel at school with THOUSANDS of Fans, but I don't think he's got many friends. I've never seen him hang out with a group of kids besides us.

How's that even possible?

He should be SWIMMING in BFFs, taking reservations for who he's gonna hang out with every single night, but... there's none of that.

I went back to my room to sit. Videogames and TV weren't really calling my name after all that. Then I saw Fergus through my window.

He was alone in his bedroom, playing checkers all by himself, spinning the board around after each move. He looked so heartbroken. Defeated. Lonely.

It's funny – a lot of times, I never know how to help someone who's down in the dumps like that, but that time, I knew exactly what to do.

It was one of the best nights I've had in forever.

EPISODE NINETEEN:
DIET KOALA AND MINTOS

FIVE HUNDO FANS!

BOOMSHAKALAKA!

But doesn't it sound better if I say I've got HALF A THOUSAND Fans? Yup. I've got half a million fans.

Anyways, more cans at my locker today means more videos to make! Today's suggestion is to set off a Diet Koala and Mintos explosion during lunch!

And just so you know, I cleared this with Principal Hawkins first. I wasn't about to coat the cafeteria with fizzy soda without asking permission.

I'm trying to get RID of the "sabotager" name, remember?

Surprisingly, Hawkins was cool with it again. He thought it'd be a wonderful way to get children to participate with blah blah blah, I don't remember exactly what he said.

Hawkins went above and beyond, too. He got Mr. Mitchell, the science teacher, to buy 30 2-liter bottles of Diet Koala and 30 packs of Mintos from Foodalicious.

And getting Mr. Mitchell to do ANYTHING fun is a big deal all by itself! I don't know what that guy's got against FUN. You'd think he'd love anything with SCIENCE written all over it, but nope. Maybe he's a robot or something.

There's a small stage at the back of the cafeteria – that's where we set up our experiment. Everybody was watching, so it wasn't hard to find 30 volunteers, each one with a pack of Mintos and a Diet Koala.

It was the talk of the school! Some classes even took a trip down to the cafeteria just to watch!

Miss Gymalski was there with a megaphone and started the countdown.

COUNTING DOWN STARTING FROM FIVE! FOUR! THREE! TWO!

*26 other kids that way →

As soon as she said, "One!" all 30 kids popped their Mintos into their soda bottles and quickly tried to twist the tops back on. The fizzing sounds that came from those bottles was enough to drown out the sounds of laughing kids.

Within seconds, every bottled started hissing like crazy, and that's when the whole cafeteria went bananas.

The bottles shot off the tables, into the air, across the room, bouncing off the walls and the floors.

It was NUTS.

In a good way.

The whole place was a warzone of ricocheting soda bottles and screaming kids. Annie got nailed right away. She flopped to the ground like a doll.

Chuck was doing all kinds of crazy ninja moves to try to fight off the bottles, but he was no match for an ambush. FOUR bottles got him at the same time, taking him out.

Many of the teachers stood against the wall behind clear tarps so they didn't get soaked but could still see the action.

The whole thing lasted about 30 seconds, but it was the most insane and messy 30 seconds of our lives.

And when it was over... everybody was laughing.

Nobody got hurt, which if you know me, you kind of come to expect a few injuries, right?

But nope. Not this time.

The stunt was perfect. It was fun.

And I got the whole thing on camera.

Okay, maybe ONE person got hurt...

PS - turns out, ninjas are easily defeated by diet soda and candy.

Who woulda thunk?

EPISODE TWENTY:
FERGUS HAS AN EVIL TWIN

During school, I asked Fergus if he had any kind of advice for an up and coming YouTube star like me. I'm not at his level yet, but at the rate my Fan count was skyrocketing, I knew it was gonna be sooner than later. He was pretty psyched that I asked.

I didn't know what he had planned, but he was so excited about it that he didn't even walk home with Annie, Chuck, and me. He bolted as soon as school dismissed so he could get things ready.

When six-o-clock rolled around, I went over to Fergus' house, eager to learn the secrets of vlogging. Fergus' mom, Mrs. Widdershim, told me he was out back, waiting. She said Chuck and Annie were out there, too, so I headed around the house.

What kind of cool stuff was Fergus gonna show me? Was he gonna teach me search engine things? How to make better thumbnails? Better titles? Gnarly editing techniques?

Turns out, he had something completely different in mind.

Chuck and Annie were off to the side, sipping sodas. They waved when they saw me. Annie tossed me a thumbs-up and then mouthed the words, "You're going to die!"

That probably wasn't a good sign.

Fergus was in the middle of his yard, wearing a black robe

with a hood that covered his face. All I could see were the whites of his eyes.

Okay.

This was NOT going to be what I thought it was.

There were tires perfectly placed on the ground, logs with balance beams on top of them, a kiddie pool filled with mud, and a bunch of other stuff that I was gonna have to get up close and personal with. There was even a bounce house at the end of it all.

Fergus had made a freaking obstacle course for me.

Before I got started, Fergus had me put on a blindfold. I did it because I thought he was gonna ask me to run through his obstacle course without being able to see anything.

Makes sense, right?

But that's not what happened.

Instead of that, Fergus started smacking me around with a yardstick, telling me that I needed to PREDICT where the next hit was gonna come from, like some kind of ninja prophet or something!

I questioned it at first, but then I remembered that Fergus was sort of a master at the vlogging game. Maybe I needed to forget everything I knew and listen to the kid.

After that, he had me crawl through the mud and under a bunch of strings while he sprayed me with water and screamed hardcore life lessons at the top of his lungs.

It was a side of Fergus I'd never seen before. And to be honest, it kind of freaked me out.

Once I was caked in mud, I had to run across the balance beams. Every time I slipped off, Fergus would smack me with his stinkin' yardstick and tell me to do it again until I made it across without falling.

And while I was struggling with torturous training, Chuck and Annie were filling their tummies with snacks that Fergus' mom had brought out for them.

I thought it was pure evil to make me watch them eat fancy schmancy desserts without me, but then I realized that it was all part of Fergus' training...

SOMEBODY WILL **ALWAYS** HAVE MORE THAN YOU! MORE FANS! MORE VIEWS! MORE COMMENTS! DO **NOT** FOCUS ON GETTING WHAT **THEY** HAVE! FOCUS ON MAKING **YOURSELF** BETTER!

BUT YOUR MOM JUST BROUGHT OUT FRESH MACARONS!

At last, I made it to the bounce house at the end of the yard, which I assumed was my reward for completing Fergus' obstacle course.

Train hard, play hard, right?

Of course, I was wrong.

Inside the bounce house was the last stage of my training. Fergus created a final boss battle for me with a LITERAL boss that I had to battle.

Oh, and did I mention that the boss was wearing a mask of my face?

Because he was wearing a mask with my face.

That was it for me. I was done. I get what Fergus was trying to do but wrestling some beefcake stranger in a bounce house was a little much, even for me.

But it didn't matter what I wanted because the wheels were already in motion.

The wrestler grabbed me before I could escape and slammed me against the walls over and over and over. Who the heck WAS this guy anyway??

The battle against myself didn't last long.

For the record, nothing snapped.

I faked it.

I can pop my shoulder on command.

It really comes in handy sometimes, like when a super buff dude keeps tossing you around like a ragdoll.

After Fergus realized I wasn't actually hurt, he gave me a high-five and said I passed his training with flying colors.

As my reward, he went inside to grab a plate of all the dessert I missed out on earlier. Chuck and Annie went to help him since there was so much of it.

I plopped down in a lawn chair to finally relax. My body was wrecked from Fergus' obstacle course.

Maxton took the chair next to mine, and we talked...

I smiled. Nodded. Said thanks.

But I think the truth is that it's the other way around...

EPISODE TWENTY-ONE:
TODAY'S THE DAY

IT'S FRIDAY – THE DAY WE FIND OUT WHO DONATED THE MOST CANS!

IF IT'S **ME**, THEN I'M JUMPIN' THE GULLY TONIGHT!

1112 VIEWS

999 FANS

The Help the Hungry assembly was going to be in the gymnasium during last period. All the students were getting out of class for it.

The rest of the school day was pretty normal. I didn't really have time to make any other videos before the assembly, so there weren't any more cans at my locker.

That was it. What I had was what I had.

And what I had was 125 cans of food. There was NO WAY I'd lose with that many. It'd probably be close between me and Dutch, but I'm pretty sure I had the win locked up.

I couldn't believe the week I'd had. I went from being a zero to a total hero in LESS than five days, can you believe that?? It's crazy that I'm only ONE Fan away from breaking 1,000. But that's how fame works sometimes. One day you're nothing, the next day you're something.

Students at Wood knew my name. They turned their heads when I walked into a room. They gave me high-fives as I walked past them. Those "Jump the Gully" shirts were everywhere now.

I finally got the thing I wanted.

I'M FAMOUS.

EPISODE TWENTY-TWO:
THE "HELP THE HUNGRY" FOOD DRIVE

AND HERE...

WE...

GO...

The gymnasium was packed with students, all laughing and shouting and messing around. Principal Hawkins was up front with every single canned good that had been donated that week.

The BMX bike was in front of it all, shiny and pretty, just waiting for me to take it home. Waiting for me to break it in by jumping it over the gully in my backyard.

I sat up front so I wouldn't have to walk far when I got called up as the winner. A bunch of kids swarmed around me because I was such a hot shot.

I get it – people wanna be around greatness.

Principal Hawkins took the mic, and everybody calmed down so they could hear him. He looked at his clipboard and said the usual, "Thank you for all your hard work blah bla-biddy blah," and started giving us stats for the week.

Altogether, the students at Wood Intermediate donated over 1,000 cans of food, which was a record for the school.

Over 1,000 cans of food is a ton of cans, but most of those are from kids who only brought two or three, Principal Hawkins explained. Then there were a bunch who brought 10 or so. A handful that brought over 20. Those numbers really added up when you had a ton of kids.

Hawkins then said there were only two students who went above and beyond in can donations. There were only two students who could possibly win the bike. Me or Dutch.

The principal had us both come to the front to make things a little more suspenseful. I don't know, it kind of seemed mean to bring Dutch up at all. What was he supposed to do after I won? Walk away in defeat?

Ouch.

That was gonna be hecka embarrassing for him. He'd probably duct tape me again for it, even though it was the principal's idea to bring him up.

Then Principal Hawkins got to the good stuff. He looked at his clipboard, and said...

The principal paused for effect leaving everybody on the edge. It was dead silent. In about one second, Hawkins was gonna say my name. The crowd would cheer. The bike would be mine. Dutch would run out crying, probably, I don't know.

My point is that I was about to win.

All my hard work and dedication to my fans was gonna finally pay off! I kept my eyes on the bike. I've never wanted anything more in my life.

The principal finally said my name, and I raised my hands in total dominating victory!

Except... that wasn't my name.

Last I checked, my name is Davy Spencer.

NOT Dutch McKenzie, so why the heck did Principal Hawkins say DUTCH McKENZIE and not DAVY SPENCER??

I couldn't believe it.

The students at Wood couldn't either. Nobody cheered. They made more of a "disappointed groan" sound. Sort of like an "Awwwwwggghh..."

Hawkins read the number of cans I donated – 125.

Then he read the number of cans DUTCH donated – 355.

Dutch won the bike, fair and square. Actually, not "fair," since he was snatching cans away from other kids all week. Seriously, where the heck were the Hall Monitors??

I slumped down in my seat as Dutch danced over to the BMX bike. A few people clapped, but it was still quiet enough to hear Dutch's tennis shoes squeaking on the floor.

Principal Hawkins encouraged everybody to stand and give Dutch a round of applause. It was the respectable thing to do, and I didn't want to be a sore loser in front of the whole school, so I stood and clapped, too.

I mean, it was a weak clap, but still a clap.

Dutch got the bike and rode circles around Principal Hawkins and me, doing victory laps and showing off. Then he rode around the rest of the gym chanting his own name.

It was awkward, hearing him chant his own name while pumping his fists in the air.

I was bummed.

But not just because I lost, but because I let my Fans down!

I really busted my butt to make videos that they wanted to see and jumping that gully would've been the perfect season finale for all those kids who had helped me out, but none of that was gonna happen now.

Honestly, I wasn't even that upset about losing the bike.

That's life.

That's the game.

But seeing Dutch win it?

I think that's what everybody in the gym was so grossed out about. Especially because he was throwing it in all our faces.

That went on for about a minute. Hawkins was trying to get Dutch to stop riding the bike, but Dutch wasn't listening. Everybody was forced to watch the kid gloat.

There was a thick feeling of disappointment in the air that everybody shared, but it might've just been muggy in there — the gymnasium doesn't have air-conditioning.

Then, all of a sudden, the craziest thing happened...

Fergus came forward.

He grabbed the microphone from Principal Hawkins, and said...

Dutch skidded the bike to a stop and stared daggers at Fergus.

Then another kid in the crowd raised his hand. And another. And another and another. Dozens of hands shot into the air.

My. Jaw. Dropped.

Kids shouted numbers across the gymnasium. Principal Hawkins scribbled furiously on his clipboard, tallying up the new total.

Annie and Chuck both had huge smiles, and then they gave me their cans, too.

The whole thing was intense, with numbers being shouted from every direction.

It was like the end of a movie when the hero loses and villain wins, but then there's suddenly this thing that happens from out of nowhere, and it gives the hero just enough juice to get back up and ABSOLUTELY shred!

And all Dutch could do was watch.

When it was all over, Dutch still had the 355 cans he donated, but my number? My number was different. My number was...

The crowd cheered.

Dutch threw my bike to the ground and stormed out of the gym.

I couldn't believe it.

The bike was mine.

I had won.

All I had left to do... was jump the gully.

EPISODE TWENTY-THREE:
JUMPING THE GULLY

HERE IT IS...
THE BIG
JUMP.

1234 VIEWS   1000 FANS

School got out right after the assembly. I was a hero. Students and teachers both congratulated me and wished me luck with the jump. I rode my new bike out of the school as students ran behind me screaming like we were in some kind of cheesy '80s movie.

Somebody asked what time I was gonna jump the gully, and since I didn't really have a plan, I said...

UM, RIGHT NOW?

I went home with a whole PARADE of kids behind me. It was so crazy, but the GOOD kind of crazy, not the bad. The BAD kind of crazy would be if a bunch of street cats followed me home.

Yeah, no. I wouldn't want that.

Nobody wants that.

Uh, anyways, as I led all my new peeps down the sidewalk, my buds all caught up to me – Annie, Chuck, and Fergus. They were super happy that I defeated Dutch, but I could tell by the looks on their faces that they were kind of stressed.

And, I don't know why, but all of a sudden I got nervous about the whole thing.

I know, I know! I'd been planning for this all week!

Telling all my Fans I was gonna jump if they helped me win!

Making video after video so they WOULD help me win!

And not one single time had I ever felt the way I did in that moment.

Scared.

But I knew I had to push those feelings WAY down in my tummy because I had a job to do and everybody was counting on me! If I bailed on the stunt, then I'd lose ALL my new Fans!

And I had a PLETHORA of them to keep happy.

A PLETHORA, I tell you, a PLETHORA!

When we got back to my place, everybody went around to the back while I went into the garage to grab my helmet. My sister was still at daycare, and both of my parents were still at work, but I didn't need any of them to tell me that safety came first.

Duh.

As I strapped the helmet to my head, Emma showed up.

Gotta be honest here – I liked the idea of her hanging out at my house. Except, maybe next time, it could be when she wasn't trying to talk me out of doing something stupid...

Crud. I couldn't answer her.

I didn't know the names of anybody else in my backyard.

Hey, when you're famous, people know YOUR name – not the other way around. And those kids waiting for me DEFINITELY knew my name because I could hear them chanting it.

I'M SORRY, BUT I GOTTA GO...

Outside, I took my place at the top of the slope that led down to the gully.

I could see the entire cardboard track that Chuck had made. The brown paper really made the green grass around it pop. Green and brown – like a Super Mario level.

People were lined up on both sides of the track. I didn't even know most of them, but I assumed they were my Fans.

I mean, why would they be there if they weren't?

There were A LOT of kids there, enough that it was "standing room only." They were all shouting at me to jump already because they were starting to get bored.

Geez... like, gimme a minute, right?

Annie, Chuck, and Fergus were off to the side. Emma had joined them, too. They were the only ones who weren't shouting at me like I was some kind of clown.

My FANS were going nuts, but my FRIENDS weren't.

I was gonna be fine, right?

Ride fast, hit the ramp hard and fly over to the other side like that kid in that alien movie.

It wasn't even that big of a jump.

I mean, personally, I'D never jumped that far before. The farthest I'd ever gotten was launching off a curb, and even then, I almost spilled.

Hmmm...

Fans were still shouting at me.

They were getting cranky.

Whatever I was gonna do, I had to do it fast, but more importantly... I had to own it. I had to make the decision and know without a shadow of a doubt that it was the right one.

So, I took a deep breath, put my hand on my bike, and said...

There were a few gasps from the crowd. Some were angry. Some felt cheated. Some figured I'd chicken out, but whatever, I didn't care.

Because my FRIENDS were already telling me I did the right thing, so boo-yah to everybody else!

That's when Dutch showed up out of nowhere.

He pushed himself through the crowd, coming at me like a crazy person. Then he grabbed my bike's handlebars and shoved me right off the seat.

He busted out a camera and started recording a video for his own channel as he pedaled down the slope toward the gully.

OMG!

HE was gonna jump the gully!

Everybody watched as Dutch hit the ramp at full speed, taking off into the sky like a rocket ship flying up, up, and away, past the clouds, and into the atmosphere...

No, I'm kidding.

Dutch flopped right over the side like a piece of raw bacon.

EPISODE TWENTY-FOUR:
THE AFTER-MATHEMATICS

I'M SAD TO SAY...

DUTCH DIDN'T MAKE IT.

30 VIEWS   27 FANS

Wait, wait, wait! I don't mean he's dead! He just didn't make the jump, but I don't think ANYBODY could have. The ramp fell apart the second Dutch touched it. Pretty sure I didn't even have a chance, so it's a good I made the super mature decision of not jumping.

Anyways, Dutch was fine, but the bike was totaled.

The whole thing was bent out of shape, still in the gully, but only because nobody was strong enough to pull it out of the mud.

That sucker's stuck there until the end of time.

And just like I thought — my Fan count sunk like a rock because I bailed on the stunt, no surprise there.

What WAS a surprise was that Dutch's Fan count EXPLODED because of course it did.

3101 VIEWS   3042 FANS

Oh well. Can't focus on what he's got. Just gotta focus on making myself better.

I've still got more Fans than I started with, so that's a plus. And the Fans who DID stick around left some pretty awesome comments.

SilentButter42 1 day ago

glad u didnt die lol keep making videos!

mattawatter81 1 day ago

You did the right thing 100%

PepperOni 1 day ago

with videos like yours, you'll go viral in no time!

I'm gonna be famous someday, I know that. It's in the stars. It's my destiny. But nobody's gonna hand it to me. I'm gonna have to put in the hard work every single day just like Fergus does.

What's really important is that I got kids to donate canned goods this week, which is INCREDIBLY awesome of me.

Like, that's SUPERHERO level of awesome.

I'm basically the same as Batman.

But even Batman needs a break, so I think I'm gonna take the rest of this season off. It's been a long week, and I've got a checkers tournament I need to get to.

But don't worry. I'll be back, for sure.

And how cool would it be if all of you, MY FANS, helped me

figure out what kind of videos to make next time??

DECIDE WHAT HAPPENS
IN THE NEXT Kid YouTuber BOOK!

Thanks for hanging out, and I'll see you next season with more crazy videos and adventures!

PEACE!

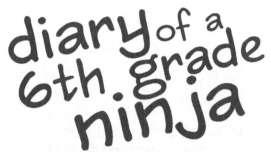

Marcus Emerson is the author and illustrator of a whole lot of books including the way popular DIARY OF A 6TH GRADE NINJA series, THE SUPER LIFE OF BEN BRAVER series, and the SECRET AGENT 6th GRADER series. His goal is to ~~make money~~ create children's books that are funny and inspirational for kids of all ages – even the adults who never grew up.

Marcus still dreams of becoming an astronaut and WALKING ON THE SUN, LIKE WHAT?? THAT'S NOT EVEN POSSIBLE.

Made in the USA
Coppell, TX
22 March 2023

14598423R10100